WILD GRASS

Lu Hsun

Wild Grass

FOREIGN LANGUAGES PRESS
PEKING 1976

First Edition   1974
Second Printing   1976

Publisher's Note

All Lu Hsun's prose poems, twenty-three in all, are contained in this collection. Written between 1924 and 1926, they were compiled by the author into one volume entitled *Wild Grass*, which was first published in 1927 by the Peihsin Bookstore, Peking.

This English translation has been made from the 1973 edition published by the People's Literature Publishing House, Peking. To help readers to understand these prose poems better, the preface Lu Hsun wrote in 1931 for an English translation of *Wild Grass*, which never appeared in print, has been included in the present edition.

Printed in the People's Republic of China

Lu Hsun's Preface, Written in 1931, for an English Edition of "Wild Grass"

Mr. Y. S. Feng has sent me through a friend his English translation of *Wild Grass** and asked me to say a few words. Unfortunately, not knowing English, I can only say a few words of my own. However, I hope the translator will not mind my doing only half of what he expected.

These twenty-odd short pieces, as the dates at the end of each show, were written between 1924 and 1926 in Peking and published successively in the periodical *Yu Ssu*. Most of them were simply occasional reflections. Because at the time it was difficult to speak outright I sometimes had to use rather ambiguous language.

To cite a few examples. "My Lost Love" was written to satirize the poems about lost loves which were then the vogue; "Revenge" was written out of revulsion at the

---

* The translator of *Wild Grass* was Feng Yu-sheng, whose English translation never appeared in print. This preface was later published by the author in *Two Hearts*, a collection of essays written in 1930 and 1931.

number of bystanders in society; "Hope" out of astonishment at the passivity of young people. "Such a Fighter" was my reaction to those men of letters and scholars who abetted the warlords. "The Blighted Leaf" was written for my friends who wanted to preserve me. After the Tuan Chi-jui government fired on unarmed demonstrators, I wrote "Amid Pale Bloodstains," at a time when I had left home and gone into hiding. "The Awakening" was written during the fighting between the warlords of the Fengtien and Chihli cliques, after which I was unable to remain in Peking.

So it may also be said that these were mostly small pale flowers on the edges of the neglected hell, which could not of course be beautiful. But this hell was bound to be lost. This was brought home to me by the expressions and tones of a handful of eloquent and ruthless "heroes" who had not at that time realized their ambitions. Thereupon I wrote "The Good Hell That Was Lost."

Later on I wrote no more things of this kind. In an age when things were changing daily, such writing, and even such reflections, were no longer allowed to exist. To my mind, this was probably a good thing. And here my preface for these translations may well end.

November 5, 1931

Foreword

When I am silent, I feel replete; as I open my mouth to speak, I am conscious of emptiness.

The past life has died. I exult over its death, because from this I know that it once existed. The dead life has decayed. I exult over its decay, because from this I know that it has not been empty.

From the clay of life abandoned on the ground grow no lofty trees, only wild grass. For that I am to blame.

Wild grass strikes no deep roots, has no beautiful flowers and leaves, yet it imbibes dew, water and the blood and flesh of the dead, although all try to rob it of life. As long as it lives it is trampled upon and mown down, until it dies and decays.

But I am not worried; I am glad. I shall laugh aloud and sing.

I love my wild grass, but I detest the ground which decks itself with wild grass.

A subterranean fire is spreading, raging, underground. Once the molten lava breaks through the earth's crust, it will consume all the wild grass and lofty trees, leaving nothing to decay.

But I am not worried; I am glad. I shall laugh aloud and sing.

3

Heaven and earth are so serene that I cannot laugh aloud or sing. Even if they were not so serene, I probably could not either. Between light and darkness, life and death, past and future, I dedicate this tussock of wild grass as my pledge to friend and foe, man and beast, those whom I love and those whom I do not love.

For my own sake and for the sake of friend and foe, man and beast, those whom I love and those whom I do not love, I hope for the swift death and decay of this wild grass. Otherwise, it means I have not lived, and this would be truly more lamentable than death and decay.

Go, then, wild grass, together with my foreword!

Lu Hsun

Written in White Cloud Pavilion, Kwangchow
April 26, 1927

Autumn Night

Behind the wall of my backyard you can see two trees: one is a date tree, the other is also a date tree.

The night sky above them is strange and high. I have never seen such a strange, high sky. It seems to want to leave this world of men, so that when folk look up they won't be able to see it. For the moment, though, it is singularly blue; and its scores of starry eyes are blinking coldly. A faint smile plays round its lips, a smile which it seems to think highly significant; and it dusts the wild plants in my courtyard with heavy frost.

I have no idea what these plants are called, what names they are commonly known by. One of them, I remember, has minute pink flowers, and its flowers are still lingering on, although more minute than ever. Shivering in the cold night air they dream of the coming of spring, of the coming of autumn, of the lean poet wiping his tears upon their last petals, who tells them autumn will come and winter will come, yet spring will follow when butterflies flit to and fro, and all the bees start humming songs of spring. Then the little pink flowers smile, though they have turned a mournful crimson with cold and are shivering still.

As for the date trees, they have lost absolutely all their leaves. Before, one or two boys still came to beat down the dates other people had missed. But now not one date is left, and the trees have lost all their leaves as well. They know the little pink flowers' dream of spring after autumn; and they know the dream of the fallen leaves of autumn after spring. They may have lost all their leaves and have only their branches left; but these, no longer weighed down with fruit and foliage, are stretching themselves luxuriously. A few boughs, though, are still drooping, nursing the wounds made in their bark by the sticks which beat down the dates: while, rigid as iron, the straightest and longest boughs silently pierce the strange, high sky, making it blink in dismay. They pierce even the full moon in the sky, making it pale and ill at ease.

Blinking in dismay, the sky becomes bluer and bluer, more and more uneasy, as if eager to escape from the world of men and avoid the date trees, leaving the moon behind. But the moon, too, is hiding itself in the east; while, silent still and as rigid as iron, the bare boughs pierce the strange, high sky, resolved to inflict on it a mortal wound, no matter in how many ways it winks all its bewitching eyes.

With a shriek, a fierce night-bird passes.

All of a sudden, I hear midnight laughter. The sound is muffled, as if not to wake those who sleep; yet all around the air resounds to this laughter. Midnight, and no one else is by. At once I realize it is *I* who am laughing, and at once I am driven by this laughter back to my room. At once I turn up the wick of my paraffin lamp.

A pit-a-pat sounds from the glass of the back window, where swarms of insects are recklessly dashing themselves against the pane. Presently some get in, no doubt through a hole in the window paper. Once in, they set up another pit-a-pat by dashing themselves against the chimney of the lamp. One hurls itself into the chimney from the top, falling into the flame, and I fancy the flame is real. On the paper shade two or three others rest, panting. The shade is a new one since last night. Its snow-white paper is pleated in wave-like folds, and painted in one corner is a spray of blood-red gardenias.

When the blood-red gardenias blossom, the date trees, weighed down with bright foliage, will dream once more the dream of the little pink flowers. . . and I shall hear the midnight laughter again. I hastily break off this train of thought to look at the small green insects still on the paper. Like sunflower seeds with their large heads and small tails, they are only half the size of a grain of wheat, the whole of them an adorable, pathetic green.

I yawn, light a cigarette, and puff out the smoke, paying silent homage before the lamp to these green and exquisite heroes.

September 15, 1924

The Shadow's Leave-Taking

If you sleep to a time when you lose track of time, your shadow may come to take his leave with these words:

"There is something I dislike in heaven; I do not want to go there. There is something I dislike in hell; I do not want to go there. There is something I dislike in your future golden world; I do not want to go there.

"It is you, though, that I dislike.

"Friend, I'll no longer follow you; I do not want to stay here.

"I do not want to!

"Ah, no! I do not want to. I would rather wander in nothingness.

"I am only a shadow. I shall leave you and sink into darkness. Yet darkness will swallow me up, and light also will cause me to vanish.

"But I do not want to wander between light and shade; I would rather sink into darkness.

"However, I am still wandering between light and shade, uncertain whether it is dusk or dawn. I can only raise my ashen-grey hand as if to drain a cup of wine. At the time when I lose track of time, I shall go far away alone.

"Alas! If it is dusk, black night will surely engulf me, or I shall be made to vanish in the daylight if it is dawn.

"Friend, the time is at hand.

"I am going to enter darkness to wander in nothingness.

"You are still expecting some gift from me. What is there for me to give? If you insist, you shall have the same darkness and nothingness. But I would like it to be only darkness, which may be lost in your daylight. I would like it to be only nothingness, which would never take possession of your heart.

"This is what I would like, friend —

"To go far away alone to a darkness from which not only will you be excluded, but other shadows too. There will be myself alone sunk in the darkness. That world will be wholly mine."

September 24, 1924

The Beggars

I am skirting a high, mouldering wall, trudging through the fine dust. Several other people are walking alone. A breeze springs up and above the wall the branches of tall trees, their leaves still unwithered, are stirring over my head.

A breeze springs up, and dust is everywhere.

A child begs from me. He is wearing lined clothes like others and does not look unhappy, yet he blocks my way to kowtow and whines as he follows me.

I dislike his voice, his manner. I detest his lack of sadness, as if this were some game. I am disgusted by the way in which he follows me, whining.

I walk on. Several other people are walking alone. A breeze springs up, and dust is everywhere.

A child begs from me. He is wearing lined clothes like others and does not look unhappy, but he is dumb. He stretches out his hands to me in dumb show.

I detest this dumb show of his. Besides, he may not be dumb; this may just be his way of begging.

I do not give him alms. I have no wish to give alms. I stand above those alms-givers. For him I have only disgust, suspicion and hate.

I am skirting a tumble-down, mud wall. Broken bricks have been piled in the gap, and beyond the wall is nothing. A breeze springs up, sending the autumn chill through my lined gown, and dust is everywhere.

I wonder what method I should use in begging. In what voice should I speak? What dumb show should I use if pretending to be dumb? . . .

Several other people are walking alone.

I shall receive no alms, not even the wish to give alms. I shall receive the disgust, suspicion and hate of those who consider themselves above the alms-givers.

I shall beg with inactivity and silence. . . .

I shall at last receive nothingness.

A breeze springs up, and dust is everywhere. Several other people are walking alone.

Dust, dust. . . .

. . . .

Dust. . . .

September 24, 1924

My Lost Love

— New Doggerel in the Classical Style

My love lives on the mountain-side,
I long to see her, but too high the mountains;
Helpless I hang my head and wet my gown
With tears that flow like fountains.
A scarf she gives me, gay with butterflies.
What shall I give her? Owls.
I know not why, but much to my surprise
She turns away and scowls.

My love lives in the heart of town,
I long to see her, but the crowd I fear;
And as I gaze up helplessly
Tears trickle down my ear.
A pair of swallows, sketched, my gift from her;
A stick of candied haws, her gift from me;
Angry, she turns her face away,
I know not why and I am all at sea.

My love lives on the river bank,
I long to see her but the stream's too deep;

12

Helpless I cock my head, and tears
Into my lapel seep.
She gives me a golden watch-chain,
I give her a diaphoretic;
Angry, she turns her face away,
I know not why and start to feel neurotic.

My love lives in a rich man's house,
I long to call there but I have no car;
Helpless I shake my head, and now my tears
Are scattered near and far.
She gives me roses, and a gift
Of brown snakes I then make her;
Angry, she turns away from me —
Why?! May the devil take her!

October 3, 1924

Revenge

Human skin is probably less than a millimetre thick, and below, through a network of blood vessels denser than the densely packed tussores which crawl one over the other up the wall, there races hot red blood, radiating warmth. And with this warmth people charm, excite and attract each other, desperately eager to cuddle, kiss and embrace so as to enjoy the intoxicating ecstasy of life.

But one stab with a sharp knife through this thin, peach-coloured skin will make the hot red blood spurt out like an arrow to flood the killer directly with all its warmth; then, the exhalation of icy breath, the sight of pallid lips, will take him out of himself, bringing him the transcendent, supreme ecstasy of life; while as for his victim, he is forever steeped in the transcendent, supreme ecstasy of life.

This being so, the two of them, stripped naked and grasping sharp knives, confront each other in the vast wilderness.

The two of them will embrace, will kill each other. . . .

From all sides passers-by hasten there, densely packed as tussores crawling up walls or ants carrying off salted fish-heads. They are smartly dressed but empty-handed. Yet from all sides they hasten there, and crane their necks desperately to feast their eyes on this embrace or slaughter. Already they have a foretaste of the sweat or blood on their own tongues when it is over.

However, the two of them confront each other in the vast wilderness, stripped naked and grasping sharp knives, neither embracing nor killing and, moreover, showing no intention of embracing or killing.

The two of them keep this up to eternity, their full, living bodies nearly atrophied, yet showing not the least intention of embracing or killing.

The passers-by become bored. They feel boredom seeping into their pores, feel boredom from their hearts seeping out of their pores to creep all over the wilderness and seep into the pores of others. Their throats and tongues become parched, their necks tired. Finally they look at one another blankly and gradually disperse, feeling so atrophied that they have even lost their interest in life.

Then all that is left is the vast wilderness, with the two of them stripped naked and grasping sharp knives in atrophied confrontation. They feast their eyes, eyes like those of the dead, on the atrophy of the passers-by, their bloodless massacre, and are steeped forever in the transcendent, supreme ecstasy of life.

December 20, 1924

Revenge (II)

Because he thinks himself the Son of God, the King of the Israelites, he is to be crucified.

The soldiers put on him a purple robe, make him wear a crown of thorns, and wish him joy. Then they beat his head with a reed, spit upon him, and bow the knee before him. After they have mocked him, they strip off his purple robe and leave him wearing his own clothes as before.

See how they beat his head, spit upon him, kneel before him. . . .

He will not drink the wine mixed with myrrh. He wants to remain sober to savour the Israelites' treatment of their Son of God, and have longer to pity their future but hate their present.

All around is hate, pitiable, execrable.

Hammering is heard, and nails pierce his palms. But the fact that these pitiable creatures are crucifying their Son of God alleviates his pain. Hammering is heard, and nails pierce the soles of his feet, breaking a bone so that pain shoots through his heart and marrow. But the fact that these execrable creatures are crucifying their Son of God comforts him in his pain.

The cross is hoisted up. He is hanging in mid-air.

He has not drunk the wine mixed with myrrh. He wants to remain sober to savour the Israelites' treatment of their Son of God, and have longer to pity their future but hate their present.

All the passers-by insult and curse him, the chief priests and the scribes also mock him, the two thieves being crucified with him ridicule him too.

Even those being crucified with him. . . .

All around is hate, pitiable, execrable.

In the pain from his hands and feet he savours the sorrow of the pitiable creatures who are crucifying the Son of God, and the joy of the execrable creatures who are crucifying the Son of God and who know that the Son of God is about to die. Sudden agony from his broken bones shoots through his heart and marrow, intoxicating him with great ecstasy and compassion.

His belly heaves in the agony of compassion and execration.

There is darkness over all the earth.

"Eloi, Eloi, lama sabachthani?" (My God, my God, why hast thou forsaken me?)

God has forsaken him, and so he is the son of man after all. But the Israelites are crucifying even the son of man.

Those who reek most of blood and filth are not those who crucify the Son of God, but those who crucify the son of man.

December 20, 1924

Hope

My heart is extraordinarily lonely.

But my heart is very tranquil, void of love and hate, joy and sadness, colour and sound.

I am probably growing old. Is it not a fact that my hair is turning white? Is it not a fact that my hands are trembling? Then the hands of my spirit must also be trembling. The hair of my spirit must also be turning white.

But this has been the case for many years.

Before that my heart once overflowed with sanguinary songs, blood and iron, fire and poison, resurgence and revenge. Then suddenly my heart became empty, except when I sometimes deliberately filled it with vain, self-deluding hope. Hope, hope — I took this shield of hope to withstand the invasion of the dark night in the emptiness, although behind this shield there was still dark night and emptiness. But even so I slowly wasted my youth.

I knew, of course, that my youth had departed. But I thought that the youth outside me still existed: stars and moonlight, limp fallen butterflies, flowers in the darkness, the funereal omens of the owl, the weeping with blood of the nightingale, the vagueness of laughter, the dance of love. . . . Although it might be a youth of sadness and uncertainty, it was still youth.

But why is it now so lonely? Is it because even the youth outside me has departed, and the young people of the world have all grown old?

I have to grapple alone with the dark night in the emptiness. I put down the shield of hope, hearing the *Song of Hope* by Petöfi Sándor (1823-49):

> "What is hope? A prostitute!
> Alluring to all, she gives herself to all,
> Until you have sacrificed a priceless treasure —
> Your youth — then she forsakes you."

It is already seventy-five years since this great lyric poet and Hungarian patriot died for his fatherland on the spears of the Cossacks. Sad though his death, it is even sadder that his poetry has not yet died.

But — so wretched is life — even a man as daring and resolute as Petöfi had in the end to halt before the dark night and gaze back towards the distant Orient.

"Despair, like hope," he said, "is but vanity."

If I must still live in this vanity which is neither light nor darkness, then I would seek the youth of sadness and uncertainty which has departed, even though it is outside me. For once the youth outside me vanishes, my own old age will also wither away.

But now there are neither stars nor moonlight, no limp fallen butterflies, no vagueness of laughter, no dance of love. The young people are very peaceful.

So I have to grapple alone with the dark night in the emptiness. Even if I cannot find the youth outside me, I would at least have a last fling in my own old age. But where is the dark night? Now there are neither stars nor moonlight, no vagueness of laughter, no dance of love. The young people are very peaceful, and before me there is not even a real dark night.

Despair, like hope, is but vanity.

New Year's Day, 1925

Snow

The rain of the south has never congealed into icy, glittering snowflakes. Men who have seen the world consider this humdrum; does the rain, too, think it unfortunate? The snow south of the Yangtze is extremely moist and pretty, like the first indefinable intimation of spring, or the bloom of a young girl radiant with health. In the snowy wilderness are blood-red camellias, pale, white plum blossom tinged with green, and the golden, bell-shaped flowers of the winter plum; while beneath the snow lurk cold green weeds. Butterflies there are certainly none, and whether or no bees come to gather honey from the camellias and plum blossom I cannot clearly remember. But before my eyes I can see the wintry flowers in the snowy wilderness, with bees flying busily to and fro — I can hear their humming and droning.

Seven or eight children, who have gathered to build a snow Buddha, are breathing on their little red fingers, frozen like crimson shoots of ginger. When they are not successful, somebody's father comes to help. The Buddha is higher than the children; and though it is only a pear-shaped mass which might be a gourd or might be a Buddha, it is beautifully white and dazzling. Held together by its own moisture, the whole figure glitters and sparkles. The children use fruit stones for its eyes, and steal rouge from some mother's vanity-case for its lips. So now it is really a respectable Buddha. With gleaming eyes and scarlet lips, it sits on the snowy ground.

Some children come to visit it the next day. Clapping their hands before it, they nod their heads and laugh. The Buddha just sits there alone. A fine day melts its skin, but a cold night gives it another coat of ice, till it looks like opaque crystal. Then a series of fine days makes it unrecognizable, and the rouge on its lips disappears.

But the snowflakes that fall in the north remain to the last like powder or sand and never hold together, whether scattered on roofs, the ground or the withered grass. The warmth from the stoves inside has melted some of the snow on the roofs. As for the rest, when a whirlwind springs up under a clear sky, it flies up wildly, glittering in the sunlight like thick mist around a flame, revolving and rising till it fills the sky, and the whole sky glitters as it whirls and rises.

On the boundless wilderness, under heaven's chilly vault, this glittering, spiralling wraith is the ghost of rain. . . .

Yes, it is lonely snow, dead rain, the ghost of rain.

January 18, 1925

Cover of the First Chinese Edition of Wild Grass

CONTENTS

The Kite

A Peking winter dismays and depresses me: the thick
snow on the ground and the bare trees' ashen branches
thrusting up towards the clear blue sky, while in the dis-
tance one or two kites are floating.

At home, the time for kites is early spring. When you
hear the whirr of a wind-wheel, you raise your head to
see a grey crab-kite or a soft blue centipede-kite. Or there
may be a solitary tile-kite, without a wind-wheel and flown
too low, looking pathetically lonely and forlorn. By this
time, though, the willows on the ground are putting out
shoots, and the early mountain peaches have budded. Set
off by the children's fancy-work in the sky, together they
make up the warmth of spring. Where am I now? All
round me dread winter reigns, while the long-departed
spring of my long-forgotten home is floating in this northern sky.

Yet I never liked flying kites. Far from liking kites,
in fact, I detested them as playthings of good-for-nothing
children. My young brother was just the reverse. He
must then have been about ten, often fell ill and was
fearfully thin, but his greatest delight was kites. Unable
to buy one and forbidden by me to fly one, he would
stand for hours at a time, his small lips parted in longing,
gazing raptly at the sky. If a distant crab-kite suddenly

23

came down, he would utter a cry of dismay; if the strings of two tile-kites became disentangled, he would jump and skip for joy. This struck me as absurd and contemptible.

One day it occurred to me I had not seen much of him lately, but I had noticed him picking up bamboo sticks in the backyard. The truth dawned on me in a flash. I ran to a small deserted store-room and, sure enough, as I pushed open the door, I discovered him there in the midst of the dusty debris. He had been sitting on a foot-stool in front of a big square stool; but now, standing up in confusion, he changed colour and shrank back. Propped up against the big stool was the bamboo framework of a butterfly-kite, not pasted yet with paper; while on the stool lay two small wind-wheels for the butterfly's eyes, which he had just been beautifying with red paper. This work was nearly done. I was pleased to have found out his secret; but furious that he could deceive me so long, while he toiled so single-heartedly to make the toy of a good-for-nothing child. I seized the framework at once and broke one of its wings, then swept the wheels to the ground and trampled on them. In size and strength he was no match for me; so of course I came off completely victorious. Then I stalked out proudly, leaving him standing in despair in that little room. What he did after that I neither knew nor cared.

But retribution came to me at last, long after our parting, when I was already middle-aged. I was unlucky enough to read a foreign book on children, from which I learned for the first time that play is a child's best occupation, and playthings his good angels. At once this childhood tyranny over the spirit, forgotten for more than twenty years, came to my mind; and that instant my heart seemed to turn to lead and sink heavily down and down.

My heart did not break; it simply sank down and down.

I knew how I could make it up to him: give him a kite, approve of his flying it, urge him to fly it, and fly it with him. We could shout, run, laugh! . . . But by this time he, like me, had long had a moustache.

I knew another way I could make it up to him: go to ask his forgiveness, and wait for him to say: "But I didn't blame you at all." Then, surely, my heart would grow lighter. Yes, this way was feasible. There came a day when we met. The hardships of life had left their marks on our faces, and my heart was very heavy. We fell to talking of childhood happenings, and I referred to this episode, admitting that I had been a thoughtless boy. "But I didn't blame you at all," I thought he would say. Then I should have felt forgiven, and my heart would henceforth have been lighter.

"Did that really happen?" He smiled incredulously, as if he were hearing a tale about someone else. It had slipped his mind completely.

The thing was completely forgotten, with no hard feelings. In that case, what forgiveness could there be? Without hard feelings, forgiveness is a lie.

What hope is there for me now? My heart will always be heavy.

Now the spring of my home is in the air of these strange parts again. It carries me back to my long-departed childhood, and brings with it an indefinable sadness. I had better hide in dread winter. But clearly all about me winter reigns, and is even now offering me its utmost rigour and coldness.

January 24, 1925

The Good Story

The lamp flame slowly dwindled, a sign that there was not much paraffin left; and the paraffin, which was not of the best brand, had already blackened the chimney with its smoke. Crackers exploded on all sides, and cigarette smoke hung round me. It was a dull, dark night.

I closed my eyes and leaned against the back of my chair, resting the hand holding *A Beginner's Notebook** on my knee.

And in this drowsy state I saw a good story.

It was a lovely, charming, enthralling story. Many beautiful people and beautiful things mingled like the cloud tapestry in the sky, flying past like a myriad shooting stars, yet stretching out into infinity.

I seem to remember rowing a small boat past an ancient highway. On both banks, reflected in the azure stream, were tallow trees and young rice plants, wild flowers, fowl, dogs, bushes and withered trees, thatched cottages, pagodas, monasteries, farmers and country women, country girls, clothes hanging out to dry, monks, coir capes, hats of bamboo splints, sky, clouds and bamboos. Following each stroke of the oar they caught the

---

* A Tang Dynasty work by Hsu Chien (659-729) and others.

26

flickering sunlight and mingled with the fish and weeds in the water, till all were swaying together. Then shadows and objects shivered and scattered, expanded and merged; but as soon as they merged they contracted once more, and approached their original form. The outline of each shadow was blurred as a summer cloud fringed with sunlight, darting out quicksilver flames. All the river I passed was like this.

And the story I now saw was like this too. With the blue sky in the water as a background, everything was intermingled, interwoven, ever moving, ever extending, so that I could not see any end to it.

The few sparse hollyhocks beneath the withered willows by the stream must have been planted by the country girls. Great crimson flowers and variegated red flowers, floating in the water, suddenly scattered and stretched out into streamers of crimson water, but with no aura. The thatched cottages, dogs, pagodas, country girls, clouds . . . were floating too. Each of the great crimson flowers stretched out now into rippling red silk belts. The belts interwove with the dogs, the dogs with the white clouds, and the white clouds with the country girls. . . . In a twinkling they would contract again. But the reflection of the variegated red flowers was already broken and stretching out to interweave with the pagodas, country girls, dogs, thatched cottages and clouds.

Now the story that I saw became clearer, more lovely, charming, enthralling and distinct. Above the clear sky were countless beautiful people and beautiful things. I saw them all, and I recognized them all.

I was about to look more closely at them. . . .

But as I was about to look more closely at them, I opened my eyes with a start to see the cloud tapestry

27

wrinkle and tangle as if someone had thrown a big stone into the water, so that waves leapt up and tore the whole image to shreds. I snatched without thinking at my book, which had nearly slipped to the floor. Before my eyes still hovered a few rainbow-hued, shattered reflections.

I really loved this good story. While some shattered reflections still remained I wanted to catch them, perfect and perpetuate them. I tossed aside my book, leaned forward and reached for my pen. But now there was not the least reflection left. All I could see was dim lamplight. I was no longer in the little boat.

But I still remember seeing this good story that dull, dark night. . . .

February 24, 1925

The Passer-by

TIME: *some evening.*

PLACE: *somewhere.*

CHARACTERS:

THE OLD MAN — *about seventy, white beard and hair, a black gown.*

THE GIRL — *about ten, auburn hair, black eyes, a gown with black squares on a white background.*

THE PASSER-BY — *between thirty and forty, tired and crabbed, with a smouldering gaze, black moustache and tousled hair; ragged black jacket and trousers, bare feet in shabby shoes. A sack on his arm, he leans on a bamboo pole as tall as he is.*

To the east, a few trees and ruins; to the west, a forlorn graveyard; between them a faint track. A little mud hut has its door open facing this track. Beside the door is a dead tree stump.

(The GIRL *is about to help the* OLD MAN *up from the stump on which he is sitting.)*

OLD MAN: Hey, child! Why have you stopped?

GIRL (*looking eastward*): There's someone coming. Look!

OLD MAN: Never mind. Help me inside. The sun is setting.

GIRL: I . . . want to have a look.

OLD MAN: What a child you are! You can see heaven, earth and the wind every day; isn't that enough for you? There is nothing else so worth looking at. Yet you want to see who's coming. Anyone who appears at sunset can't do you any good. . . . We'd better go in.

GIRL: But he's already quite close. Ah, it's a beggar.

OLD MAN: A beggar? That isn't likely.

(*The* PASSER-BY *limps out from the bushes on the east, and after a moment's hesitation walks slowly up to the* OLD MAN.)

PASSER-BY: Good evening, sir.

OLD MAN: Thank you. Good evening.

PASSER-BY: Sir, may I make so bold as to ask for a cup of water? I am parched after walking, and there's not a pool or water-hole to be found.

OLD MAN: Yes, that's all right. Please sit down. (*To the* GIRL.) Child, fetch some water. See that the cup is clean.

(*The* GIRL *walks silently into the hut.*)

OLD MAN: Please sit down, stranger. What is your name?

PASSER-BY: My name? That I don't know. Ever since I can remember, I've been on my own; so I don't know my real name. As I go on my way, people call me by this name or that as the fancy takes them. But I can't remember them, and I have never been called by the same name twice.

OLD MAN: I see. Well, where are you from?

PASSER-BY (*hesitating*): I don't know. Ever since I can remember, I have been walking like this.

OLD MAN: All right. Then may I ask you where you are going?

PASSER-BY: Of course you may. The thing is, I don't know. Ever since I can remember, I have been walking like this, on my way to some place ahead. All I can remember is that I have walked a long way, and now I have arrived here. I shall push on that way (*he points west*) ahead!

(*The GIRL carefully carries out a wooden cup of water and gives it to him.*)

PASSER-BY (*taking the cup*): Thank you, lass. (*He drinks the water in two gulps, and returns the cup.*) Thank you, lass. It is rare to meet with such kindness. I really don't know how to thank you.

OLD MAN: There is no need to be so grateful. It won't do you any good.

PASSER-BY: No, it won't do me any good. But I feel much better now. I shall push on. You must have been here for quite a long time, sir. Do you know what kind of place that is ahead?

OLD MAN: Ahead? Ahead are graves.

PASSER-BY (*startled*): Graves?

GIRL: No, no no! There are ever so many wild roses and lilies there. I often go there to play, to look at them.

PASSER-BY (*looking west, appears to smile*): Yes, there are many wild roses and lilies there; I have often gone there myself to enjoy looking at them. But those are graves. (*To the* OLD MAN.) Sir, what lies beyond the graveyard?

OLD MAN: Beyond the graveyard? That I don't know. I have never been beyond.

PASSER-BY: You don't know!

GIRL: I don't know either.

OLD MAN: All I know is the south, the north and the east where you come from. Those are the places I know best, and they may be the best places for such as you. Don't take offence at what I say, but you are already so tired I think you would do better to go back; because if you keep on you may never reach the end of your journey.

PASSER-BY: I may never reach the end? . . . (*He thinks this over, then starts up.*) Impossible! I must go on. If I go back, there's not a place without celebrities, not a place without landlords, not a place without expulsion and cages, not a place without sham smiles and hypocritical tears. I hate them. I am not going back.

OLD MAN: You may be wrong. You may come across some tears that spring from the heart, some genuine compassion.

PASSER-BY: No. I have no wish to see the tears that spring from their hearts. I do not want their compassion.

OLD MAN: In that case, (*he shakes his head*) you will have to go on.

PASSER-BY: Yes, I have to go on. Besides, there is a voice ahead urging me on and calling me so that I cannot rest. The trouble is my feet are so gashed and cut through walking that I've lost a good deal of blood. (*He raises one foot to show the* OLD MAN.) I haven't got enough blood; I need to drink some. But where can I find it? Besides, I don't want to drink just anyone's blood. I have to drink water instead to make up for it. There is always water on the way; indeed I have never felt any lack of it. But my strength is draining away just because there is too much water in my blood. And if I walked less far today it's because I found not a single small water-hole.

OLD MAN: That may not be the reason. The sun has set; I think you had better rest for a while, like me.

PASSER-BY: But the voice ahead is telling me to push on.

OLD MAN: I know.

PASSER-BY: You know? You know that voice?

OLD MAN: Yes. It seems to have called to me before as well.

PASSER-BY: The same voice that is calling me now?

OLD MAN: That I can't say. It called me several times, but I ignored it, so then it stopped; that's all I can remember.

PASSER BY: Ah, you ignored it. . . . (*He thinks this over, gives a start and listens.*) No! I must go on. I can't rest. It's a pity that my feet are in such bad shape. (*He prepares to leave.*)

GIRL: Here! (*She gives him a piece of cloth.*) Bandage your feet.

PASSER-BY: Thank you, lass. (*He takes the cloth.*) Really. . . . Really such kindness is rare. With this I can walk further. (*He sits down on some rubble and is about to bind the cloth round his ankle.*) No, this won't do. (*He struggles to his feet.*) Take it back, lass. It's not enough for a bandage. Besides, this is really too kind, and I don't know how to thank you.

OLD MAN: No need to thank her; it won't do you any good.

PASSER-BY: No, it won't do me any good. But to me this is the finest alms of all. Look, can you see anything comparable on me?

OLD MAN: You need not take it so seriously.

PASSER-BY: I know. But I can't help it. I'm afraid this is my way. If I were to receive alms, I would be like a vulture catching sight of a corpse and hovering overhead, longing to see her destruction with my own eyes. Or I might call down destruction on everything except her, myself included, for I myself deserve it. But I'm not yet strong enough for that. Even if I were, I wouldn't want her to come to such an end, because such an end is one they mostly dislike. I think this way is soundest. (*To the* GIRL.) This piece of cloth is perfect, but a bit too small. So I'll give it back to you.

GIRL (*falling back, frightened*): I don't want it! Take it.

PASSER-BY (*with something like a smile*): Ah. . . . Because I've held it?

GIRL (*nods and points at his sack*): Keep it in there, for fun.

PASSER-BY (*stepping back in dismay*): But how am I to walk with this on my back?

OLD MAN: It's because you won't rest that you can't carry anything. Rest a while, then you'll be all right.

34

PASSER-BY: That's right, a rest. . . . (*He reflects, then gives a start and listens.*) No, I cannot! I had better go.

OLD MAN: You don't want to rest?

PASSER-BY: I do.

OLD MAN: Well then, rest a while.

PASSER-BY: But I cannot. . . .

OLD MAN: You still think you had better go on?

PASSER-BY: Yes, I had better go on.

OLD MAN: Very well, you must go then.

PASSER-BY (*stretching himself*): Good, I'll say good-bye then. I am very grateful to you. (*To the* GIRL.) I'll give this back to you, lass. Please take it back.

(*Frightened, the* GIRL *draws back her hand and wants to take refuge in the hut.*)

OLD MAN: Take it. If it's too heavy, you can throw it away in the graveyard any time.

GIRL (*steps forward*): Oh no, that won't do!

PASSER-BY: No, that won't do.

OLD MAN: Well then, hang it on one of the wild roses or lilies.

GIRL (*claps her hands, laughing*): Good!

PASSER-BY: Ah. . . .

(*For a second there is silence.*)

OLD MAN: Good-bye then. Peace be with you. (*He stands up and turns to the* GIRL.) Child, help me inside. Look, the sun has already set. (*He turns to the door.*)

PASSER-BY: Thank you both. May peace be with you. (*He takes a few steps, deep in thought, then starts.*) But I cannot! I must leave. I had better go. . . . (*Raising his head, he walks resolutely towards the west.*)

(*The* GIRL *helps the* OLD MAN *into the hut, then* *shuts the door.* *The* PASSER-BY *limps on towards the wilderness, and night falls behind him.*)

March 2, 1925

Dead Fire

I dreamed that I was running along the mountain of ice.

It was a huge, towering mountain, reaching to the icy sky above; and the sky was flooded with frozen clouds, each fragment like a fish scale. At the foot of the mountain was the forest of ice, with leaves and branches like the pine and cypress. And all was icy cold, pale as ashes.

But suddenly I fell into the valley of ice.

All around, above and below, was icy cold, pale as ashes. Yet over the pallid ice lay countless red shadows, interlacing like a web of coral. Looking beneath my feet, I saw a flame.

This was dead fire. It had a fiery form, but was absolutely still, completely congealed, like branches of coral with frozen black smoke at their tips which looked scorched as if fresh from a fire-place. And so, casting reflections upon the ice all around and being reflected back, it had been turned into countless shadows, making the valley of ice as red as coral.

Aha!

As a child, I always liked to watch the foam ploughed up by swift ships or the fiery flames belched out from a blazing furnace. Not only did I like to watch them, I

longed to see them clearly. The pity was they kept changing all the time, and never retained a fixed form. However hard I gazed, I was never left with a clear-cut
impression.

Dead flame, now at last I had you!

As I picked up the dead fire to examine it closely, its
iciness seared my fingers; but enduring the pain I thrust
it into my pocket. The whole valley instantly turned as
pale as ashes. At the same time I wondered how to leave
this place.

From my body wreathed a coil of black smoke, which
reared up like a wire snake. Instantly crimson flames
began flowing everywhere, hemming me in like a great
conflagration. Looking down, I discovered the dead fire
was burning again, had burnt through my clothes and
was flowing on the icy ground.

"Ah, friend!" it said. "You awoke me with your
warmth!"

I immediately hailed it, and asked its name.

"I was abandoned by men in the valley of ice," it said,
ignoring my question. "Those who abandoned me have
already perished and vanished. And I was nearly frozen
to death by that ice. If you had not warmed me and
made me burn again, before long I should have perished."

"I am glad you have awoken. I was just wondering
how to leave this valley of ice, and I would like to take
you with me so that you may never be frozen but go on
burning forever."

"Ah, no! Then I should burn out."

"I should be sorry if you were to burn out. I had better
leave you here."

"Ah, no! I should freeze to death."

"What is to be done then?"

"What will you do yourself?" it countered.

"As I told you, I mean to leave this valley of ice."

"Then I had better burn out!"

It leapt up like a red comet, and together we left the valley. Suddenly a large stone cart drove up, and I was crushed to death beneath its wheels, but not before I saw the cart fall into the valley of ice.

"Aha! You will never meet the dead fire again." I laughed with pleasure as I spoke, as if pleased that this should be so.

April 23, 1925

The Dog's Retort

I dreamed I was walking in a narrow lane, my clothes in rags, like a beggar.

A dog started barking behind me.

I looked back contemptuously and shouted at him: "Bah! Shut up! Lick-spittle cur!"

He sniggered.

"Oh no!" he said. "I'm not up to man in that respect."

"What!" Quite outraged, I felt that this was the supreme insult.

"I'm ashamed to say I still don't know how to distinguish between copper and silver, between silk and cloth, between officials and common citizens, between masters and their slaves, between. . . ."

I turned and fled.

"Wait a bit! Let us talk some more. . . ." From behind he urged me loudly to stay.

But I ran straight on as fast as I could, until I had run right out of my dream and was back in my own bed.

April 23, 1925

40

The Good Hell That Was Lost

I dreamed I was lying in bed in the wilderness beside hell. The deep yet orderly wailing of all the ghosts blended with the roar of flames, the seething of oil and the clashing of iron prongs to make one vast, intoxicating harmony, proclaiming to all three regions the peace of the lower realm.

Before me stood a great man, beautiful and benign, his whole body radiant with light; but I knew he was the devil.

"This is the end of everything! The end of everything! The wretched ghosts have lost their good hell." He spoke with indignation and grief, then sat down to tell me a story that he knew.

"It was when heaven and earth were made honey-coloured that the devil overcame god, and wielded absolute power. He held heaven, earth and hell. Then he came in person to hell and sat in the midst of it, radiating bright light over all the ghosts.

"Hell had long been neglected: the spiked trees had lost their glitter, the verge of the boiling oil no longer seethed, at times the great fires puffed out merely a little blue smoke, and far off there still bloomed some mandrake flowers, very small, pale and wretched. But that was not to be wondered at, for the earth had been fearfully burnt and had naturally lost its fertility.

"Awaking amid the cold oil and lukewarm fires, by the light of the devil the ghosts saw the small flowers of hell, so pale and wretched, and were completely bewitched. They suddenly remembered the world of men, and after reflecting for none knows how many years, they uttered towards mankind a great cry denouncing hell.

"Man responded and arose, upholding the right he fought against the devil. Louder than thunder, the tumult of fighting filled all three regions. At last, by dint of great guile and cunning snares, he forced the devil to withdraw from hell. After the final victory, the flag of mankind was hoisted over the gate of hell.

"The ghosts were still rejoicing together when man's emissary to reorganize hell arrived. He sat down in the middle of hell, invested with the majesty of man, and ruled over the ghosts.

"When the ghosts uttered another cry denouncing hell, they became rebels against man. Condemned to eternal damnation for this crime, they were banished to the midst of the spiked trees.

"Man then wielded absolute power over hell, his authority exceeding that of the devil. He re-established order, having given the highest post to the Ox-headed Demon. He also added fuel to the fires, sharpened the sword hills and changed the whole face of hell, doing away with the former decadence.

"At once the mandrake flowers withered. The oil seethed as before, the swords were sharp as before, the fires blazed as before, and the ghosts groaned and writhed as before, until none of them had time to regret the good hell that was lost.

"This was man's success, the ghosts' misfortune. . . .
"Friend, I see you mistrust me. Yes, you are a man.
I must go to look for wild beasts and demons. . . ."

June 16, 1925

The Epitaph

I dreamed I was standing before the stone tablet of a tomb, reading the inscriptions on it. The tablet, made apparently of sandstone, was crumbling away and overgrown with moss. The fragments left of the inscriptions read:

"... contracted a chill while singing and roistering; saw an abyss in heaven. In all eyes saw nothing; in hopelessness found salvation. ...

"... There is a wandering spirit which takes the form of a serpent with poisonous fangs. Instead of biting others, it bites itself, and so it perishes. ...

"... Begone! ..."

Not until I went round to the back of the tablet did I see the solitary grave. No plants grew on it, and it was in ruins. Through a large gap I saw the corpse, disembowelled, its heart and liver gone. Yet its face bore no trace of either joy or sorrow, but had the inscrutability of smoke.

Before I could turn away in doubt and dread, my eye fell on the mutilated inscription on the back of the tablet:

". . . I tore out my heart to eat it, wanting to know its true taste. But the pain was so agonizing, how could I tell its taste? . . .

". . . When the pain subsided I savoured the heart slowly. But since by then it was stale, how could I know its true taste? . . .

". . . Answer me. Or, begone! . . ."

I was eager to be gone. But the corpse had sat up in the grave. Without moving its lips, it said:

"When I turn to ashes, you will see me smile!"

I hurried away, not daring to look back, for fear I should see it coming after me.

June 17, 1925

Tremors of Degradation

I dreamed that I was dreaming. I had no idea where I was, but before me was the interior of a tightly closed cottage late at night, and yet I could also see the dense growth of stonecrop on the roof.

The globe of the paraffin lamp on the wooden table had been newly polished, making the room very bright. In this light, on the rickety couch, under the hairy, muscular flesh of a stranger, a slight frail body trembled with hunger, pain, shock, humiliation and pleasure. The skin, slack but still blooming, glowed; the pale cheeks flushed faintly, like lead painted with liquid rouge.

And the lamp flame too shrank with fear, for the east was already light.

However, the air was still pervaded, pulsating, with a wave of hunger, pain, shock, humiliation and pleasure. . . .

"Ma!" A little girl of about two, awakened by the door creaking open and shut, cried out from the floor in one corner of the room screened off by a straw mat.

"It's still early. Go back to sleep," urged her mother, disconcerted.

"I'm hungry, ma. My tummy aches. Will we have anything to eat today?"

"Yes, we will. When the pieman comes, I'll buy you some sesame cakes." For reassurance she tightened her grip on the small silver coin in her hand, her low voice trembling with grief as she went to the corner of the room, moved away the matting, picked up the child, and laid her on the rickety couch.

"It's still early. Go back to sleep." As she spoke she raised her eyes helplessly towards the sky visible above the tumble-down roof.

Suddenly another great wave sprang up in the air, colliding with the first and whirling to form a maelstrom which swallowed up everything, myself included, so that I was unable to breathe.

I woke up groaning. Outside the window all was silver moonlight. Dawn still seemed far away.

I had no idea where I was, but since before me was the interior of a tightly closed cottage late at night, I knew that this was the continuation of my last dream. However, many years had passed in the dream. The cottage was well kept now inside and out; within it, a young couple and a troop of children resentfully and contemptuously confronted an elderly woman.

"All because of you, we can't face the world," the man fumed. "You imagine you raised her, but in fact you ruined her. It would have been better for her to starve to death while she was small."

"You wrecked my whole life," cried the woman.

"And involved me too," said the man.

"Involved them as well." His wife pointed to the children.

The youngest, who was playing with a dry reed, now brandished it like a sword and shouted:

"Kill!"

The elderly woman's lips twitched convulsively, she started, then calmed down, and presently she was standing there as impassively as a stone statue. She opened the door and walked out into the depth of night, leaving behind her all derisive taunts and vicious laughter.

She walked on and on through the depth of night till she reached the boundless wasteland. All around lay wasteland, with only the sky high above and neither bird nor insect flying past. Stark-naked, like a stone statue, she stood in the centre of the wasteland and the whole past flashed through her mind: hunger, pain, shock, humiliation and pleasure . . . she trembled; ruin, wreck and involvement . . . she twitched convulsively; "Kill!" . . . she calmed down. . . . In another flash she pieced it all together: devotion and estrangement, loving care and revenge, nurture and annihilation, blesses and curses. . . . She raised both hands then with all her might towards the sky and from her lips escaped a cry half-human, half-animal, a cry not of the world of men and therefore wordless.

When she uttered this wordless cry, her whole body, great as a statue but already wasting and degraded, was shaken by tremors. These tremors, small and distinct at first as fish-scales, started seething like water over a blazing fire; and at once the air too was convulsed like waves in the wild, storm-racked ocean.

Then she raised her eyes to the sky, and her wordless cry was swallowed up in silence. Only her tremors, radiating like sunbeams, set the waves in the air whirling round as if in a cyclone to sweep headlong across the illimitable wasteland.

It was a nightmare, yet I knew this was because I had pressed my hands on my chest. And in my dream I strained every nerve to remove these overpowering, heavy hands.

June 29, 1925

On Expressing an Opinion

I dreamed I was in the classroom of a primary school preparing to write an essay, and asked the teacher how to express an opinion.

"That's hard!" Glancing sideways at me over his glasses, he said: "Let me tell you a story —

"When a son is born to a family, the whole household is delighted. When he is one month old they carry him out to display him to the guests — usually expecting some compliments, of course.

"One says: 'This child will be rich.' Then he is heartily thanked.

"One says: 'This child will be an official.' Then some compliments are made him in return.

"One says: 'This child will die.' Then he is thoroughly beaten by the whole family.

"That the child will die is inevitable, while to say that he will be rich or a high official may be a lie. Yet the lie is rewarded, whereas the statement of the inevitable gains a beating. You. . . ."

"I don't want to tell lies, sir, neither do I want to be beaten. So what should I say?"

"In that case, say: 'Aha! Just look at this child! My word. . . . Oh, my! Oho! Hehe! He, hehehehehe!' "

July 8, 1925

After Death

I dreamed I had died by the roadside.

Where I was, how I came to be there, or how I had died, all this was a mystery. Anyway, by the time I knew I had died, I was lying there dead.

I heard magpies cry, then crows. The air was very fresh — though it carried a tang of the soil — it must be nearly dawn. I tried to open my eyes, but the lids would not move, as if they simply did not belong to me. Then I tried to raise my hands, and it was the same.

I felt a sudden stab of fear through my heart. When I was alive it used to amuse me to think: If a man's death were simply the paralysis of his motor nerves while sensation still remained, that would be more frightful than total death. Who could tell that my prophecy would come true, or that I was to testify to its truth myself?

I heard footsteps: someone was passing by. A wheelbarrow was pushed past my head; its load was probably heavy, for its squeaking and creaking grated on my nerves and set my teeth on edge. Then everything seemed to turn crimson: the sun must have risen. So I must be facing east. Not that it mattered. A babble of human voices — curious onlookers. They raised a cloud of dust which flew up my nose and made me want to sneeze. I was unable to, though; I just wanted to.

Then came the sound of more and more footsteps, all of which stopped beside me, and there was more whispering: quite a crowd had gathered. I felt a sudden longing to hear what they were saying. But just then I remembered how in my lifetime I used to say that criticism was not worth troubling about. Perhaps I didn't mean what I said: no sooner was I dead than I betrayed myself. But though I went on listening, I could not reach any conclusion, for the remarks seemed little more than this:

"Dead, huh? . . ."

"Uhhuh! . . ."

"Well! . . ."

"Dear me. . . . Too bad. . . ."

I was delighted not to hear a single familiar voice. Otherwise, some might grieve for me, some might be glad; some might have more to gossip about after dinner, thus wasting precious time; and all this would make me feel very bad. Now no one had seen me, so no one would be affected. Good. After all I had done no one any harm!

But then an ant, I think, started crawling on my back and made me itch. Since I could not stir, I had no means of getting rid of it. Normally, just by turning over I could have made it retreat. Now there was another one on my thigh as well! What do you think you are doing, silly insects!

Things went from bad to worse: there was a buzz and a fly landed on my cheekbone. It took a few steps, then flew to lick the tip of my nose. "I am not a celebrity, sir," I thought ruefully. "You don't have to seek me out to find material for your gossip column. . . ."

But I could not speak out. It came down from the tip of my nose to lick my lips with its clammy tongue, and I wondered if this was a declaration of love. Some others gathered on my eyebrows. At each step they took, my hair was shaken to its roots. This was going too far — much too far.

With a sudden gust of wind, something covered me from above and they all flew off. As they left I heard them say:

"What a pity! . . ."

I nearly passed out with indignation.

I was brought to myself by the thud of something wooden dropped on the ground and the shaking of the earth. On my forehead I could feel lines made by the straw matting. Then the matting was removed, and at once I felt again the burning heat of the sun.

"Why should he die *here*?" I heard someone ask.

The voice was so near that the speaker must be bending over me. But where should a man die? I used to think that although a man could not choose where to live on this earth, he could at least die wherever he pleased. Now I learned this was not the case, and it was very hard to please everyone. What a pity I had long had no pen and paper; but even if I had, I could not write; and even if I wrote, I had nowhere to publish an article. So I had to let it go.

Some men came to carry me off, but I did not know who they were. From the clashing of scabbards I guessed there were police here too, in this place where I should not have died. I was turned round several times, felt myself lifted and set down again, then heard a lid being closed and nails hammered in. But, strangely enough, they used two nails only. Did they always use two nails only in the coffins here?

"I shall be knocking into six walls this time," I thought. "I'm nailed in as well. This is really the end. It's all up with me! . . ."

"It's stuffy in here. . . ," I thought.

As a matter of fact, I was much calmer than before, though I could not be sure whether I had been buried or not. The back of my hand touched the lines on the straw matting, and I felt this type of shroud was not too bad. I was only sorry I did not know who had paid for me out of charity. But curse those wretched fellows who had put me in the coffin! One corner of my shirt was creased under my back, but they had not pulled it straight for me, and now it was sticking into me most uncomfortably. Do you think a dead man has no feelings that you act so carelessly? Pah!

My body seemed much heavier than during life, thus its pressure on the creased shirt made me much more uncomfortable than it normally would have. However, I thought I should soon get used to it, or else I should soon rot; thus it should not prove too troublesome. In the meantime I had better meditate quietly.

"How are you, sir? Are you dead?"

The voice was most familiar. When I opened my eyes, I saw it was the messenger from Pokuchai Bookshop. I had not seen him for more than twenty years, but he still looked the same as before. I examined the six sides of my coffin: they were really extremely crude and completely unpolished, the sawn edges still very rough.

"Never mind, that doesn't matter," he said, unwrapping a bundle tied in dark blue cloth. "Here is a Ming

55

Dynasty edition of Kung-yang's *Commentaries** for you. It's Chia Ching period,** and has black margins. Just keep it. And this. . . ."

"You!" I gazed in amazement at his eyes. "Are you mad?" I asked. "Can't you see what condition I'm in? What use do I have for Ming Dynasty editions?"

"That doesn't matter. Never mind."

I closed my eyes at once in irritation. For some time there was not a sound, no doubt he was gone. But then it seemed another ant started crawling up my neck and finally reached my face, where it circled round my eyes.

I never imagined men could change their ideas even after death. Suddenly a force shattered the peace of my heart, and many dreams unfolded before my eyes. Some friends had wished me happy, some enemies had wished me blotted out. Yet I had been neither happy nor blotted out, but had lived on somehow obscurely, not fulfilling the expectations of either side. And now I had died like a flitting shadow, without the knowledge even of my foes, unwilling to give them a little pleasure which would cost me nothing. . . .

In my exultation I wanted to cry. These would be my first tears after death.

No tears came, though, after all. There was a sort of flash before my eyes, and I sat up.

July 12, 1925

---

* Commentaries on *The Spring and Autumn Annals*.
** 1522-62.

56

Such a Fighter

There will be such a fighter!

No longer ignorant as the African natives shoulder-ing well-polished Mausers, nor listless as the Chinese green-banner troops* carrying automatic pistols. He does not rely on armour made of ox-hide or of scrap-iron. He has nothing but himself, and for weapon nothing but the javelin hurled by barbarians.

He walks into the lines of nothingness, where all that meet him nod to him in the same manner. He knows that this nod is a weapon used by the enemy to kill with-out bloodshed, by which many fighters have perished. Like a cannon-ball, it renders ineffective the strength of the brave.

Above their heads hang all sorts of flags and banners, embroidered with all manner of titles: philanthropist, scholar, writer, elder, youth, dilettante, gentleman. . . . Beneath are all sorts of surcoats, embroidered with all manner of fine names: scholarship, morality, national culture, public opinion, logic, justice, oriental civiliza-tion. . . .

---

*During the Ching Dynasty Han troops, who were poor fighters, were distinguished by green banners.

But he raises his javelin.

Together they give their solemn oath that their hearts are in the centre of their chests, unlike the case of other prejudiced people. They try to prove by their breast-plates that they themselves believe their hearts are in the centre of their chests.

But he raises his javelin.

He smiles and hurls his javelin to the side, and it pierces them through the heart.

All crumble and fall to the ground, leaving only a surcoat in which there is nothing. The nothingness has escaped and won the victory, because now he has become the criminal who killed the philanthropist and the rest.

But he raises his javelin.

He walks with great strides through the ranks of nothingness, and sees again the same nods, the same banners and surcoats. . . .

But he raises his javelin.

At last he grows old and dies of old age in the lines of nothingness. He is not a fighter after all, and the nothingness is the victor.

In such a place no war-cry is heard, but there is peace. Peace. . . .

But he raises his javelin!

December 14, 1925

The Wise Man, the Fool and the Slave

A slave did nothing but look for people to whom to pour out his woes. This was all he would and all he could do. One day he met a wise man.

"Sir!" he cried sadly, tears pouring down his cheeks. "You know, I lead a dog's life. I may not have a single meal all day, and if I do it is only husks of sorghum which not even a pig would eat. Not to say there is only one small bowl of it. . . ."

"That's really too bad," the wise man commiserated.

"Isn't it?" His spirits rose. "Then I work all day and all night. At dawn I carry water, at dusk I cook the dinner; in the morning I run errands, in the evening I grind wheat; when it's fine I wash the clothes, when it's wet I hold the umbrella; in winter I mind the furnace, in summer I wave the fan. At midnight I boil white fungus, and wait on our master at his gambling parties; but never a tip do I get, only sometimes the strap. . . ."

"Dear me. . . ." The wise man sighed, and the rims of his eyes looked a little red as if he were going to shed tears.

"I can't go on like this, sir. I must find some way out. But what can I do?"

"I am sure things will improve. . . ."

"Do you think so? I certainly hope so. But now that I've told you my troubles and you've been so sympathetic and encouraging, I already feel much better. It shows there is still some justice in the world."

A few days later, though, he was in the dumps again and found someone else to whom to pour out his woes.

"Sir!" he exclaimed, shedding tears. "You know, where I live is even worse than a pigsty. My master doesn't treat me like a human being; he treats his dog ten thousand times better. . . ."

"Confound him!" The other swore so loudly that he startled the slave. This other man was a fool.

"All I have to live in, sir, is a tumble-down, one-roomed hut, damp, cold and swarming with bedbugs. They gorge on me when I lie down to sleep. The place is stinking and hasn't a single window. . . ."

"Can't you ask your master to have a window made?"

"How can I do that?"

"Well, show me what it's like."

The fool followed the slave to his hut, and began to pound the mud wall.

"What are you doing, sir?" The slave was horrified.

"I am opening a window for you."

"This won't do! The master will curse me."

"Let him!" The fool continued to pound away.

"Help! A bandit is breaking down the house! Come quickly or he will knock down the wall! . . ." Shouting and sobbing, the slave rolled frantically on the ground. A whole troop of slaves came out and drove away the fool.

Roused by the outcry, the last one to come slowly out was the master.

"A bandit tried to break down our house. I was the first one to give the alarm, and together we drove him away!" The slave spoke respectfully and triumphantly.

"Good for you!" The master praised him.

Many callers came that day to express concern, among them the wise man.

"Sir, because I made myself useful, the master praised me. When you said the other day that things would improve, you were really showing foresight." He spoke very hopefully and happily.

"That's right. . . ," replied the wise man, and seemed happy for his sake.

December 26, 1925

The Blighted Leaf

Reading Satula's* poems by lamplight, I have come across a dry, pressed maple leaf.

This carries me back to late autumn of last year. There was heavy frost one night and most of the trees shed their leaves, while one small maple in my courtyard turned crimson. I paced round the tree to take a good look at the leaves, which I had never examined so closely when they were green. Not all of them had turned red; indeed, most were a pale puce, and some still had dark green spots on a crimson background. There was one in which an insect had made a hole, which, fringed with black, stared at you like some bright eye from the chequered red, yellow and green.

"This leaf has been blighted!" I thought.

So I plucked it and slipped it inside the book I had just bought. I suppose I hoped to preserve for a little time this blighted motley of colours so soon to fall, to prevent its drifting away with the other leaves.

But tonight it lies yellow and waxen before my gaze, its eye less bright than last year. In a few more years, when its former hues have faded from memory, I may

---

* Satula (1272-?), a Mongolian poet of the Yuan Dynasty.

62

even forget why I put it in the book. It seems the chequered tints of blighted leaves soon to fall can remain in my keeping for the shortest time only — to say nothing of those lush and green. Through my window I see that the trees which can best withstand cold are already denuded of leaves, much more so the maple. In late autumn there may have been blighted leaves like last year's; but, unhappily, this year I had no time to appreciate autumn tints.

December 26, 1925

Amid Pale Bloodstains

*— In Memory of Some Who Are Dead,
Some Who Live, and Some Yet Unborn.**

At present the creator is still a weakling.

In secret, he causes heaven and earth to change, but dares not destroy this world. In secret, he causes living creatures to die, but dares not preserve their dead bodies. In secret, he causes mankind to shed blood, but dares not keep the bloodstains fresh forever. In secret, he causes mankind to suffer pain, but dares not let them remember it forever.

He provides for his kind only, the weaklings among men; using deserted ruins and lonely tombs to set off rich mansions; using time to dilute pain and bloodstains; each day pouring out one cup of slightly sweetened bitter wine — not too little nor too much — to cause slight intoxication. This he gives to mankind so that those who drink it can weep and sing, seem both sober and drunk,

---

* This was written after the March 18 Incident, when the northern warlord, Tuan Chi-jui, ordered the police to fire on students and peaceful citizens of Peking, who were demonstrating against Japanese, British and American imperialist provocations. Forty-seven people were killed, and a hundred and fifty injured.

64

conscious and unconscious, appear willing to live on and willing to die. He must make all creatures willing to live on. He has not the courage yet to destroy mankind.

A few deserted ruins and a few lonely tombs are scattered over the earth, reflected by pale bloodstains; and there men taste their own vague pain and sorrow, as well as that of others. They will not spurn it, however, thinking it better than nothing; and they call themselves "victims of heaven" to justify their tasting this pain and sorrow. In apprehensive silence they await the coming of new pain and sorrow, new suffering which appals them, which they none the less thirst to meet.

All these are the loyal subjects of the creator. This is what he wants them to be.

A rebellious fighter has arisen from mankind, who, standing erect, sees through all the deserted ruins and lonely tombs of the past and the present. He remembers all the intense and unending agony; he faces squarely the whole welter of clotted blood; he understands all that is dead and all that is living, as well as all that is being born and all that is yet unborn. He sees through the creator's game. And he will arise to resuscitate or else destroy mankind, these loyal subjects of the creator.

The creator, the weakling, hides himself in shame. Then heaven and earth change colour in the eyes of the fighter.

April 8, 1926

The Awakening

Like students going to school, the planes on their bomb-ing missions fly over Peking each morning.*   And each time I hear their engines attack the air I feel a certain slight tension, as if I were witnessing the invasion of Death, though this heightens my consciousness of the exist-ence of Life.

After one or two muffled explosions, the planes drone and fly slowly off.   There may be some casualties, but the world seems more peaceful than usual.   The tender leaves of the poplar outside the window gleam dark gold in the sunlight; the blossom of the flowering plum is more glorious than yesterday.   When I have cleared away the newspapers lying all over my bed and wiped off the light grey dust which gathered on the desk last night, my small, square study continues to live up to the description, "bright windows and spotless desk."

For some reason or other, I start to edit the manu-scripts of young writers which have accumulated here. I want to go through them all.   I read them in chrono-

---

*In April 1926, when General Feng Yu-hsiang was fighting the northern warlords Chang Tso-lin and Li Ching-lin, the latter's planes came several times to bomb Peking.

logical order, and the spirits of these young people who scorn to use any veneer rise up in turn before me. They are fine, they have integrity — but, ah! they are so unhappy! They groan, become angry, and finally grow rough, my lovely youngsters.

Their spirits are roughened by the onslaught of wind and dust, for theirs is the spirit of man, a spirit I love. I would gladly kiss this roughness dripping with blood but formless and colourless. In elegant, far-famed gardens filled with rare blossoms, demure and rosy girls are leisurely whiling away the time as the stork gives a cry and dense white clouds rise up. . . . This is all extremely enthralling, but I cannot forget I am living in the world of men.

And this suddenly reminds me of an incident: Two or three years ago, I was in the staff room at Peking University when a student whom I did not know came in. He handed me a package, then left without a word; and when I opened it, I found a copy of the magazine *Short Grass*.* He said not a word, yet what a speaking silence, and what a rich gift that was! I am sorry *Short Grass* is not coming out any more; it seems merely to have served as the forerunner of *The Sunken Bell*,** And *The Sunken Bell* is tolling alone in the caverns of wind and dust deep at the bottom of the human sea.

Though the wild thistle is virtually crushed to death, it will still bear one tiny flower. I remember how moved Tolstoy was by this, how it made him write a story. Of course, when plants in the arid desert reach out desperately with their roots to suck the water deep below the

---

* A literary quarterly started by young writers in 1924.

** A literary weekly which appeared in the autumn of 1925.

ground and form an emerald forest, they are struggling for their own survival. Yet the tired, parched travellers' hearts leap up at the sight, for they know they have reached a temporary resting place. Indeed, this evokes deep gratitude and sadness.

Under the heading "Without a Title," in lieu of an address to the reader, the editors of *The Sunken Bell* wrote: "Some people say our society is a desert. If this were really the case, though rather desolate it should give you a sense of tranquillity, though rather lonely it should give you a sense of infinity. It should not be so chaotic, gloomy and above all so changeful as it is."

Yes, the young people's spirits have risen up before me. They have grown rough, or are about to grow rough. But I love these spirits which bleed and suffer in silence, for they make me know I am in the world of men — I am living among men.

While I have been editing the sun has set, and I carry on by lamplight. All kinds of youth flash past before my eyes, though around me is nothing but dusk. Tired, I take a cigarette, quietly close my eyes in indeterminate thought, and have a long, long dream. I wake with a start. All around is still nothing but dusk; cigarette smoke rises in the motionless air like tiny specks of cloud in the summer sky, to be slowly transformed into indefinable shapes.

April 10, 1926

野　草

鲁　迅　著

*

外文出版社出版（北京）
1974年（34开）第一版
1976年第二次印刷
编号：（英）10050—800
00045
10—E—30P